Definition

A body of water covering less than 10 surface acres and less than 20-feet deep is a "pond." Most any reservoir with more than 10 acres shall be considered a "lake."

But it's important to know that these guidelines are subject to change and geographic in nature.

Example: In serious fish talk, you call your five-acre impoundment a "lake." If your neighbor has the same size puddle on his place, it's a "pond."

—Mark McDonald

Basic Pond Management

First in the
Pond Boss
How-To series

By Bob Lusk
with
Mark McDonald

Pond Boss Press
DeSoto, Texas

Published by Pond Boss Press
DeSoto, Texas

Printed in the United States of America
Page production by T & T Editorial, Houston, Texas
Editorial support by Kathleen Reese, Dallas, Texas

ISBN: 0-9630964-0-1

About the Front Cover

This scenic five-acre pond hidden in the woods of northeastern Texas may be owned by conservationist Tom Malouf of Wills Point, Texas. Then again, it could be located near your home. In any case, this small impoundment, typical of what can be developed in private waters with thoughtful planning and patience, produces good fishing in a peaceful setting.

At lower left, it's true that Bruce Benedict of Jawtec Worms in Forney, Texas manufactures lures and fishes the pro bass circuit. Still, he can seldom resist the pure fun of fishing a well-managed pond.

Dedication

To the earnest folks who stare into blue-green waters. To fishermen, conservationists, fish farmers, shade-tree biologists and dreamers. Together, individually, we share the same longing to understand what we can not readily see below the surface.

Acknowledgements

✱ Dr. James Davis, Texas Agricultural Extension Service fisheries biologist, for the spirit of science and giving freely of it. To his colleagues, Dr. Ken Johnson, a leading authority on fish disease, and biologist Don Steinbach, who were both willing teachers at Texas A&M.

✱ Harrell Arms, fish farmer, consultant, knower of things large and small, Proctor, Texas, for his moral support.

✱ Bus Hartley, an octogenarian but still a student of fish, Kingman, Kansas, the first to successfully spawn catfish in culture ponds.

✱ Gary Valentine, U.S. Soil Conservation Service biologist, Temple, Texas, for twisted humor and straight information.

✱ Malcolm Johnson, III of San Marcos, Texas and Mac McCune of Richmond, Texas for their technical assistance in lake biology, but mostly for their early support of Pond Boss when it was needed most.

✱ Texas Agriculture Extension biologist Billy Higginbotham of Overton, Texas, and Texas Parks and Wildlife biologists Clell Guest and Bobby Farquhar, both of Fort Worth, Texas, for thoughtful, practical counsel on lake management principles—and going slowly enough for the co-author to understand.

✱ Victor G. McDonald, age 93, retired steelworker, Santa Cruz, Calif., who taught his grandson early the value of the written word.

✱ Don Harris of Dallas, Texas for invaluable production advice. He can hook them, all right, but with a 3-iron, not a fishing rod.

✱ The now-defunct *Dallas Times Herald* (R.I.P.), whose death in December, 1991, combined with quota hiring practices in the newspaper industry, forced the co-author to build his own pond.

Table of Contents

Table of Contents

Introduction

My earliest memories come from hikes in the woods. Actually, these were short walks into the northern Texas countryside near my home in Fort Worth, but to me, they were high adventure, journeys into the unknown.

I would stare down at a rock in the footpath and wonder if another human had ever set foot here before. One trek in particular stands out.

I was walking down a narrow path in the woods, just west of Granbury, Texas, carrying a minnow bucket full of shiners behind a seasoned woodsman of 14. I was 12 at the time, so to me he was veteran. He could walk through the woods without tangling his rod tip on overhanging trees. Boy, he was good!

Now, I already had begun learning to fish in a small creek in northeast Tarrant County, always catching a mud cat or a bream on an earthworm, but this would be different. We were going after big game—the largemouth bass. Just thinking about hooking one of those giant fish and envisioning it tail-walking across the surface took weight from that minnow bucket.

It's strange how our early experiences become adult passions. One of mine formed that day. This was in a pasture in Hood County, but it could have been any one of a million private lakes and ponds in the southern and southwestern part of the United States.

To this day, I can still see that red and white plastic float bobbing on the surface, with a two-inch shiner dangling in the water two feet below. I'll never forget the way it disappeared.

Nor will I forget the way the king of warm-water predator fish danced across the top of the water, dragging against everything my push-button Zebco 202 could offer. Before that day ended, my rural buddy, Jimmy Ramsey, and I lugged out 12 bass from 3/4 to 1 1/2 pounds. Back at his barn, with his dad's help, we cleaned our catch and bragged about our achievement.

I still remember how those bass fought, how they left shallow cuts on my thumb and forefinger as I learned to "lip" those fish. But, most of all, I remember the way my heart pounded, just being that close to one of nature's majestic creatures. This was my call of the wild.

Not long after, in the summer of 1969, my parents made a decision that would influence how and where I live, what I stand for, how I think, and what I do to earn a living.

They bought a parcel of land right on the banks of the Brazos River, several miles below a giant new reservoir called Lake Granbury. Along this river, especially near Mitchell Bend, a curious ninth-grader began to learn some of the facts of life—aquatic life, that is.

Seventy-two consecutive weekend trips to the river made it possible for a city kid to get countrified, to see different types of fish in the Brazos and to see for the first time how they lived, how they fit together in a community.

At night, while poling upriver in a 10-foot aluminum johnboat with a Coleman lantern dangling over the front, I could see channel catfish. I was intrigued by how they reacted to moon phase. In full moonlight, they hid under rocks, with just their tails sticking out. In the dark of the moon, these same fish could be seen darting everywhere. By day, they completely disappeared. What a mystery!

It was interesting to see huge schools of minnows playing follow-the-leader in the shallow rapids, to see giant gar gliding slowly along the surface of the slow-moving pools, and the seasonal journeys of sand bass coming up river from Lake Whitney each spring to spawn. Right then and there, I made up my mind to learn all I could about fish. It would not be a hobby; I decided it would be my career.

From Richland High School in 1973, it was on to Tarrant County Junior College for a temporary attempt to follow my father's footsteps in real estate. In no time, though, I was back in biology courses and aquatic labs, this time at Texas A&M University in the department of Wildlife and Fisheries Sciences.

Sheepskin finally in hand, I set out to solve world hunger and follow a passion. In 1980, after the U.S. Fish and Wildlife Service and the Texas Parks and Wildlife Department stopped stocking private waters, a new flame began to flicker— the need for fish to stock private lakes and ponds. With guidance from Gary Valentine of the Soil Conservation

Biologist Bob Lusk has been studying fish and their behavior since he was a boy, but he admits he learns something new almost every day he's in the field.

Service, as well as Jim Davis, Don Steinbach, and Ken Johnson of the Texas Agricultural Extension Service, I got more involved in lake and pond stocking than in commercial fish farming.

Thanks to seasoned gamefish producers such as Bus Hartley of Kingman, Kansas and Harrell Arms from Proctor, Texas, we learned how to properly handle delicate species such as fingerling bass and bluegill. I began to realize how much I needed to learn.

And right away I saw it was no longer enough just to stock a lake with fish. Once the fish were introduced, what then?

The answer came not long after when I served on a committee within the Texas Chapter of the American Fisheries Society that developed "Stocking Recommendations for Texas Farm Ponds," a guideline for successful stocking rates in small impoundments. Soon after, in 1984, I served as president of the trade association for fish culturists in Texas, called the Fish Farmers of Texas at the time, now known as the Texas Aquaculture Association. I've been a TAA board member since 1982.

By 1984, managing fish, not raising them, was my specialty. A move to Whitesboro, Texas, just south of the Red River on the Oklahoma border, gave me all the hatchery pond space I needed to raise sportfish and to manage private lakes and ponds exclusively.

Today, it is not hard to see the need for our products and service. America is dotted with small impoundments under private management. There are more than 900,000 private lakes and ponds in Texas alone, by Soil Conservation Service estimates.

Imagine. If just 1 percent are managed properly, that's 891,000 lakes that still need attention. And I find that most people have similar problems and concerns. As I travel the Southwest, spreading the gospel on pond management, I find myself answering the same questions, over and over.

Ironically, most of the answers wheel around a few basic principles of nature, much of it relating to those early lessons on the Brazos River.

I remember, in 1983, being contacted by a group of dedicated sportsmen in South Texas who operated a ranch with an intensive deer management program. For deer, they spared no expense, but for fish, their 50-acre lake went virtually ignored.

After surveying the reservoir, I recognized a common problem—skinny bass, all about eight or 10 inches long. I urged my South Texas friends to reduce competition for food and cover by eliminating more than 3,000 bass. Meanwhile, I stocked about 1,500 adult bluegill and redear sunfish at the beginning and initiated a fertilization program.

Five years later, they had a fishing haven, where catching 4- to 6-pound bass was common. What a turnaround!

True, not everyone has this patience or this diligence. But this is just one example of the tremendous improvement I see in the general health and productivity of lakes under management. Every year, it seems that more people are "getting green"—promoting ecology, wildlife habitat and the environment.

There is still much to be done, much to be learned. In the smallest of ponds or the largest of lakes, the quality of the resource and the fish can always be improved. This book was written to help you do just that.

—Bob Lusk, February 1993

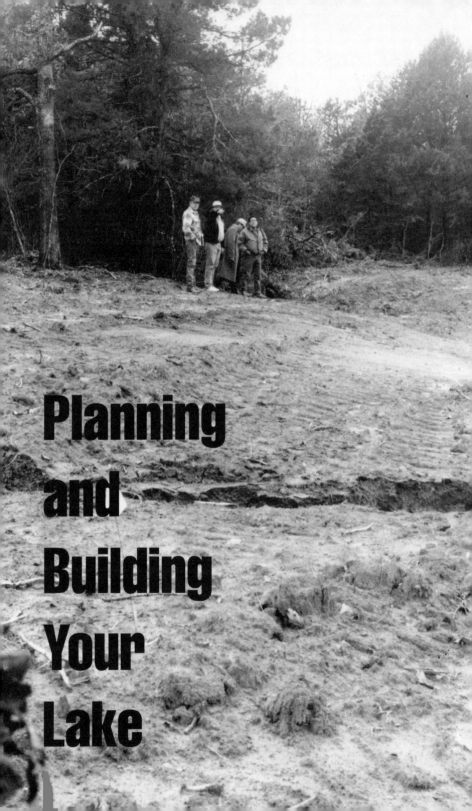

Planning and Building Your Lake

So you want to build a lake and stock it with fish. Right now, the lake of your dreams looks more like a dry creekbed or goat pasture—which, of course, it is. Nothing wrong with that, but in your mind's eye, you see a scenic place that looks as if it came off the front of a postcard, and it's spilling over with fish.

The trick is getting from Point A to Point B, from the harsh reality of the present to the fish factory you'd like in the future. You long for that summer weekend when the kids could be catching bass and catfish at the same time your family and friends are serving hamburgers, served at a cook-out right on the shoreline.

But the practical side of your brain has the other half spinning at 5,000 RPM. How do I accomplish my goal? Do I need an engineer, or just somebody who can run a bulldozer? Where do I turn for advice? Does the Soil Conservation Service work with people other than farmers? Could a fisheries biologist help me?

These questions force would-be pond owners to take a cold, hard look at their objectives, but it's better to turn back now before the first spade of dirt is moved. In the end, however, the real trick to turning some of your property into an eye-pleasing, productive fishing hole is no trick at all. It's a logical progression, beginning with a firm foundation of planning, not unlike constructing a skyscraper. With that weekend cook-out/fishing trip in mind, let's start at the start.

Pond construction and watershed management begin with choosing a site. This could be the single most important decision you make through the whole exercise of lake management. Remember, the best private lakes in North America were not accidents of man or nature. Great fishing and a healthy environment don't just happen. They developed over time, from a solid plan of action.

Look for land you consider to be marginal for crops or

Some of the nation's best lakes began like this, as modest-looking holes in the ground.

that's considered wasteland. Areas of erosion and rapid drop are often the best sites for damming a creek. A flattish knob, flanked by native brush or trees, can be sculpted with the dozer blade to build a pond. See the questions surfacing already? Consult your nearest Soil Conservation Service office for aerial photographs, topographical maps and soil analysis of your area. The SCS also has the technical skills to help you design and engineer your lake.

Unfortunately, budget cuts and increased work loads often leave SCS field personnel stretched thinly across the drumhead of public demand. Ask for the pond planning and construction bulletins in your state. Ask for basic soil analysis and for advice on your options. These printed materials will help channel both your water, and your thinking.

True, the local SCS agent can provide a wealth of free information, but invariably, he or she is hopelessly overscheduled. Look at this federal agency as a starting place, a source for early direction. Certainly the price is right. Then consider hiring a private engineer. Doing the project right the first time may save you money in the long run.

Check with your state and local authorities before beginning to impound surface water. In many states, this is strictly regulated. In Texas, for example, a landowner may impound no more than 199 acre feet in a single reservoir without a permit. And the permitting process can get tedious.

Know your rights, but also learn your local limitations. This could save you headaches later.

With or without government intervention in plans, often as not your wallet will dictate the size a pond. Within financial reason, plan the biggest and best lake you can afford. Once the impoundment matures and begins producing food and recreation, you won't be disappointed. It's always disheartening to survey a pond site that floods because the landowner wanted to spend only $200 building the lake, and wound up with a lake that is too small for its drainage area.

Well-managed ponds, like this one in the shadows of downtown Dallas skyscrapers, are where you find them.

Regardless of size or budget constraints, soil type becomes a major factor in planning and building your lake. Your site must have at least 30 percent clay content in the soil or it may not hold water, according to published recommendations from federal soil scientists. Clay particles swell on contact with water. Without them in the soil, you have little hope of capturing water for your lake.

Size is another key factor in the future success of your

lake, though your total acreage and the breadth of the local watershed will make some of the decisions for you.

Learn the average annual rainfall for your area, then take into account the amount of evaporation yearly. This will give strong clues as to how large and how deep your lake must be to hold water year-round.

Take, for instance, eastern New Mexico. This region may be good for raising peanuts and irrigated cotton, but some years it receives less than 10 inches of rain, while giving up more than 90 inches to evaporation. This rough calculation tells us that we must have a deep basin, or face the prospect of a dry pond.

R unoff is a pivotal point here. If we know that only four or five inches of that rain will be in the form of runoff, we have decisions to make. Remember this: It takes 27,000 gallons of water to cover an acre of land with one inch of water.

If all we get in our imaginary pond site is 4 to 5 inches of drainage, how big of a watershed do we need to build a two-acre pond? How deep should it be? Considering the rapid evaporation, we know we will have at least a net loss of 80 inches a year. That's 6 feet, 8 inches—sucked into the clouds.

If we expect to have plenty of storage capacity to account for drought conditions, the pond probably needs to be more than 20 feet deep. If we have 20 feet of depth, covering two surface acres, that gives us 40 acre feet of water. Multiply the 40 acre feet times 12 inches per foot, and you see that it takes 480 inches of runoff to fill our pond.

If we get 4 inches of runoff, that means we need to drain 120 acres of runoff just to make a two-acre pond. From an engineering standpoint, you see why you don't need extremely deep ponds in, say, Georgia.

For contrast, look at a situation in Paris, Texas, along the Red River between Oklahoma and Texas, not far from where I live in Whitesboro. The area often receives nearly 60 inches of rain per year, with less than 40 inches of evaporation. In region, if it isn't raining, it's getting ready to.

Given this annual gain in rainfall, storage capacity is not as critical. For the same two-acre pond we're using as a model, we do not need such a deep lake basin, nor do we require as much runoff from the watershed. In my consulting work, I've seen areas where a pond site needs only one acre of runoff for each acre of pond.

Here's where the SCS can give you the best advice. If an agent is unavailable, trust the judgment of a consulting biologist or an engineer.

In planning a pond of any size, maximum depth figures into your total storage capacity, of course. But you may be surprised to learn that water depth along the shoreline plays a key role in controlling weeds and producing big fish.

Shallow water encourages unwanted aquatic vegetation, the species that can clog the surface, tie up nutrients, interrupt boating and ruin the aesthetics. Do your best to minimize the amount of shallow water.

Pond Boss rule of thumb: Design your lake so that most of your water is at least three feet deep, even along the perimeter. This eliminates sunlight penetration to the bottom, the

The alert pond owner starts his new reservoir with the best in technical advice. Plan your work, then work your plan. Notice the flags posted to outline the eventual water level on this new lake.

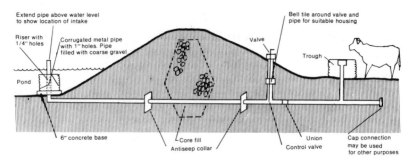

Illustration courtesy of Soil Conservation Service, U.S. Dept. of Agriculture

Water may be piped from the lake (left), through the dam's drainpipe into the a trough for livestock. This illustrates traditional pond engineering and design.

source of many tough problems with moss.

After you have selected the best site, get an engineer to survey the site to determine how much dirt to move, where the water will run and how much water the site will hold. "Shoot the grades," we call it.

This procedure will also tell you how to position the dam and where the water level will be when the lake fills. Positioning the dam may wind up a financial decision, as well as an engineering evaluation.

Here's why: Bulldozer work is most cost efficient if you need to move dirt less than 50 yards. If the dirt must be moved farther, consider hiring a scraper or earth-mover.

Just as the engineer can help you decide where to put the dam, he can offer advice on the proper slope of your shorelines. He also will help you figure how large an emergency spillway you need, and where to put it.

While your engineer shoots the grades and levels, take time to outline the pond or lake by driving short wooden stakes in the ground. This gives a point of reference during construction.

Meanwhile, ask the contractor to provide a blueprint of your dam. This will tell the dirt contractor how much earth must be moved. If the contractor understands the purpose for building the lake and realizes where the dirt will come from, he can give you a much better estimate of cost. You will be charged by the cubic yard.

Here's where a fisheries biologist should advise you and the dirt contractor in deciding what trees, brush and rock piles to leave in the lake basin for fish habitat.

Once actual work begins on the dam, here's a quick bit of advice: At this point, if you have any qualms about what you are doing, step back and evaluate. Do it now, before a potential problem becomes too time consuming and expensive to solve.

Along the way, watch your contractor "core" the dam, as he begins constructing the dam from below natural ground level, to obtain a good seal. A dam built on top of the ground is more likely to leak than one started 18 inches below ground and compacted upward.

To manage your lake for good fishing, you need to be able to control the level of the water.

Compacting the dirt on the dam and in the lake basin itself helps the soil—remember the clay particles?—hold water.

If you intend to manage your lake for fish, waterfowl, environment, or wildlife, you need to be able to control the level of the water. A bottom-water release pipe serves this function.

One of your management tools will be your ability to drop the lake level—to control unwanted aquatic vegetation, to allow for wildlife plantings for winter or just to get ready for spring rains. The bottom-water release pipe also takes water from the bottom of the lake each time the lake overflows. This is significant because the deepest water is also the most stagnant.

A lake with only an overflow spillway or with a pipe

through the dam at the top only allows the fresh water from rainfall to leave the lake. The bottom-water release pipe needs anti-seep collars to prevent leakage around the pipe. Confirm this installation with your biologist or engineer, or you may end up with a leaky dam.

After the dam site is cored and the bottom-water release pipe is in place, actual construction of the dam commences full force.

Ask your contractor about the slope of the dam. Most professionals agree that a lake should be built with a minimum of a 3-to-1 slope, sometimes even 4-to-1. Anything steeper will tend to erode, slough and compromise the structure.

Ever seen a road embankment next to a new bridge begin to collapse after heavy rains? You don't want this happening to your dam.

Some consider a 3-to-1 slope to be too steep to be safely maintained with a tractor and brush hog. Thus, many lakes are built with a 3-to-1 slope inside the lake and a 4-to-1 slope on the backside of dam for ease of maintenance.

Let's look at another important consideration known as "freeboard," the distance from the crown of the dam to the water level.

The size of the lake compared to the watershed determines the freeboard. Flood-control reservoirs constructed by the Soil Conservation Service often have 15 to 20 feet of freeboard. This is because these lakes are designed to have a large amount of storage capacity to hold back flood-producing rains and to allow orderly discharge of the water downstream without stress to the watershed directly below. Designed properly, a lake constructed for fish needs much less freeboard.

Every lake needs an emergency spillway to manage water from excessive rainfall and flooding situations. The emergency spillway is usually one foot above the overflow pipe on lakes designed for recreation and fishing. The best constructed spillways are wide with a very gentle slope away from the dam.

A spillway should not be constructed where it carries water over the dam to the back toe. Many dams have been needlessly eroded because of this. If this happens and is left uncorrected, the dam eventually will burst. The amount of freeboard needed between the crown of the dam and the spillway is determined by how much water the spillway will handle. Your engineer can help with this calculation.

If your lake lies in acid soils and the water is typically soft, now is the time to add lime to the lake by broadcasting the quantity of limestone prescribed by your agent or consulting biologist. This will balance the pH of the water and make it more conducive to raising fish.

S peaking of raising fish, that's where the fun begins. As far as I'm concerned, the planning and building stages are intriguing in their own right. But they are merely necessary means to an end.

For me, the play part of managing a lake enters the picture when the pond owner takes a long look at his goals, his wallet and his water and begins making decisions on what fish to stock, when and why.

Knowing Your Critters

What fish do you want in your pond? Only by knowing the difference between fish species can you make wise management decisions.

Once you learn about each type of fish, it becomes easier to understand the role of those fish in the aquatic community. Let's take each commonly used fish, describe it, and explore the function of these fish in management strategy.

After that, we'll look at some of the undesirable species we often call trash fish, and discuss the impact these fish have.

First, let's look at the minnows used in private ponds and lakes. The two most common ones are **FATHEAD MINNOWS** and **GOLDEN SHINERS.**

The fathead is a small, slow-moving minnow that commonly inhabits the same waters as bass and bluegill. Their function in management is to provide the first year's food source for young bass in a newly stocked body of water.

Fatheads seldom grow much longer than three

Fathead Miinnow

inches and they lack the ability to get away from predator fish, making them a prime menu item for bass, channel catfish and hybrid stripers.

Fatheads spawn by sticking eggs underneath solid objects. The male guards the nest, doing its best to ward off intruders. This fish gets its name because the male, during the spawn, exhibits soft, fleshy, little "horns" on the head. The male's color darkens and focus turns to reproduction. Talk about fatal attraction! The fathead male, hell-bent on reproducing, seemingly forgets about eating and uses all its energy to extend the bloodline and literally spawns itself to death.

After the female lays the eggs, its leaves the nest to feed

and begin regenerating more eggs. Fathead females reportedly spawn 4 to 5 times a year, dropping 400 to 500 eggs each time. More amazingly, though, the first hatch of the spring will be spawning later that same year.

No wonder the fathead is readily available virtually coast to coast through fish farmers and dealers who sell to the sportfishing side of pond management.

Fathead minnows, also known as "tuffies," feed actively on plankton and small insects and plant material. Fatheads do best in fertile water supplemented with regular feeding.

With no predator fish to keep their population in check, a few fatheads may mushroom to phenomenal numbers in a single year. Stock a few pounds per acre in the winter and by the next Thanksgiving, you may have several hundred pounds of forage, just waiting to ring the dinner bell for your hungry bass.

G olden shiners are quite a bit different than fatheads and serve a contrasting role in lake management. They grow to be much larger than their fathead cousins, often reaching seven inches long, and swim much quicker. This size and speed puts them ahead of fatheads in the underwater chow line, but still well behind the top-line predators.

Shiners most often are used in lakes and ponds being managed for largemouth bass, especially in areas where the water has a tendency to draw down for long periods. Once established, shiners often can survive long enough to reproduce and provide forage for bass.

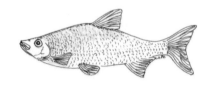

Golden Shiner

The golden shiner spawns by sticking its eggs to grassy plants in shallow water, generally around the perimeter of the pond. This fish spawns only once a year, during spring when water temperatures reach 70 to 72 degrees.

Shiners typically run in large schools of similar size fish, feeding on insects, large planktonic organisms—even small fish. They love worms and bottom-dwelling larvae, such as dragonfly nymphs. As a full-grown adult, the shiner may compete as predator, too, and with a menu list limited only by the size of its mouth. It is not uncommon to catch one by hook and line.

O ne popular pond species is the **BLUEGILL.** In a lake where prey-predator numbers are balanced, the bluegill is the only species biologists know that can generate an adequate food supply for the resident largemouth bass. Every good bass lake I've ever seen has bluegill sunfish in abundance.

There are several strains of bluegill, though they may be lumped together in references to

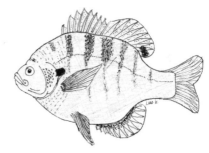

Bluegill

perch or bream. By any name, this member of the sunfish family may be found in virtually every body of fresh water in North America and generally serving the same role.

In some areas, the bluegill seldom grows longer than six or seven inches. In others, the same fish may reach 10 to 14 inches long and weigh two and a half, even three pounds, providing a sporty challenge for the light-tackle angler. The coppernose in particular has become quite popular, mostly because it often reaches 10 to 12 inches in length and a pound in weight and because of the way it graces a plate.

A staple sunfish in Dixie, the coppernose is almost as aggressive as the bass, and like the bass will jump when hooked. No wonder this colorful fish has developed a following all its own, especially among fly and light-tackle enthusiasts.

As different as they are in name and markings, bluegills share similar spawning habits. They nest in colonies, making several small craters 10 to 12 inches in diameter in the shallows. There may be 20 to 40 of these bare craters in a given area.

At peak spawning periods, each nest has a male bluegill guarding it, watching over his nest of eggs or newly hatched fry, until they are large enough to feed and fend for themselves.

Bluegill usually live in schools, often in brush. They become so aggressive that they will approach anything small that lands on the water surface. While most fish avoid a noisy disturbance, bluegill seem to be drawn by it.

Bluegill love insects, both the land-based bugs and aquatic varieties. It's important to note that bluegill will come readily to fish food. Because they share similar habitat with bass, bluegill have a tendency to shrink in number during the course of the year, depending on the size and quantity of bass in the lake. Supplementary feeding may help the bluegill population stay in shape to support your bass.

R edear sunfish are also an important animal to consider. Sometimes called shellcracker, Georgia bream or stumpknocker, these fish have been traditional favorites in the Gulf Coast states, but recent stocking efforts have pushed the fish into the Midwest as well.

Generally, the redear leads an entirely different lifestyle and grows larger than the bluegill. Indeed the world record redear,

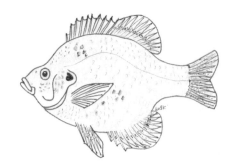

Redear

from Merritt's Mill Pond in Florida in 1986, weighed 4 pounds, 13 ounces. An incredible specimen.

In your lake, the redear will eat crustaceans, snails and thick shelled insects and small crawfish. They will not, however, take any kind of commercial fish food pellet.

Strangely, documented pond studies have shown that

where bluegill and redear are stocked side by side, the bluegill gains weight and grows rapidly, while the redear may starve, simply because the food they require may not be available. In similar studies, the reverse may be true. In planning your strategy, you will want to know these fish complement each other.

Redear spawn only once, in the spring, just a matter of weeks before the bluegill. This is one of nature's magic ways of maintaining the genetic integrity of the species and limiting natural hybridization. Redear spawn like bluegill, using nests like craters in shallow water.

Redear serve an important function in that they eat snails, which carry several parasites that attack fish, including the yellow grub. Next time you catch a bass with little yellow knots at the base of its fins and tail or meat, you might consider stocking the redear. As the redear controls the snail population, you may see fewer parasite problems.

Speaking of the freshwater king…the **LARGEMOUTH BASS** in private waters traditionally has been the most sought-after, most actively managed, most revered and, yes, perhaps the most misunderstood species in the entire ecosystem.

The bass is a widely distributed species, found throughout much of North America. Its markings range from the color of milk to the dark green of freshly printed dollar bills. It is commonly called green trout, black bass or, when it grows to 10 pounds or more, a hawg.

No matter what you may call it, this bully of the waterways remains a favored target of anglers and, as such, stands as the marquee attraction for most private waters. If a pond boss manages his or her lake for fishing, chances are, the bass plays a key role.

The largemouth is an ambush feeder that seems to ask only two questions before chowing down: Is it alive? Will it fit in my mouth?

Bass, like bluegill, spawn over shallow-water nests on firm bottom. An adult female of two pounds may lay 4,000 to

6,000 eggs, though larger bass will lay far more than that.

Many people are under the impression that bass reproduce more than once a year. Fact is, a large bass of, say, six pounds, will spawn before a smaller one, but may not lay all of her eggs at once because the tiny bubble-like organisms mature at different times.

The female develops one batch of eggs a year. The bass spawn on cycles of the moon, so the window of opportunity to release the eggs sometimes is too short to spawn all the eggs. Days later, after the remaining eggs have matured, the female may make a second or third trip back to the spawning nest.

Another yarn that may be true dictates that the bass spawn begins the first full moon after the bullfrogs come out. Bullfrogs

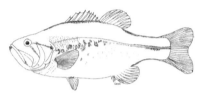

Largemouth Bass

emerge from winter hibernation of sorts at roughly the same temperature a bass spawns—70 to 74 degrees.

Once the eggs hatch, they stay in a tight school, not leaving the nest until they use up their yolk sac. A newly hatched fish has a tail, a head with two small dark eyes, and a pronounced, yellow belly—the yolk sac. The yolk sac provides nourishment for the first few days after hatching to allow the young fish to grow and develop survival skills.

As the yolk sac is used up, the fish must begin to seek food, or it will die, either by starvation or in the jaws of another predator. On the other hand, healthy bass fry, less than two weeks after hatching, begin their role as the hunter, feeding on plankton and tiny insects. In fact, it is common for bass to feed on their very own brothers and sisters in the same spawn.

It's a lesson in reality to see a bass four inches long with the tail of a three-inch relative dangling from its maw. Talk about survival of the fittest!

Survivors of this real-life underwater drama are the most

aggressive, successful predators. This is nature's selection process, and keeps bass from overpopulating their own territory. These fingerling bass grow very rapidly, up to six inches in the first 90 days, doubling their weight every few days.

Yearling bass hang out in schools for a couple of reasons. Perhaps the fish carries an instinctive sense of security in numbers. Maybe a large predator fish interprets a school of fish as one giant fish. This much is certain: Young bass enjoy an advantage when they feed as a school, working as one to flush small baitfish from their hiding places to end up as quick meals.

But as bass get larger, their schooling instincts begin to diminish. Once a bass reaches two pounds or so, it seldom travels in schools, and then only when actively searching for food. Instead, the bass becomes more territorial in its hunting as it grows older and larger. Most large bass lurk near brush, rock piles, fallen logs, standing timber, even piers and boat docks, but generally with quick access to deep water.

For most lunker bass, this is year-round behavior, and they adjust their depth slightly, depending on variables such as temperature, pH level, presence of dissolved oxygen and food supply. Also, big bass move to shallow water for spawning, where most anglers find them most vulnerable.

Researchers have identified several strains of largemouth bass over the years. The genetic family most commonly found in the U.S. has come to be known by biologists as the native or northern strain. In Cuba, California, Texas, and throughout Dixie, the so-called Florida bass rules the aquascape. This fish gets lots of ink from the sporting press, and deservedly so.

Generally, the native bass has a more streamlined body structure compared to the football shape of the Florida bass. Its markings may be lighter green and less distinct, even when the two fish occupy the same waters. Anglers insist the Florida bass is more wary of boating traffic and disturbances, a claim that has biologists working to find the ultimate "dumb fish." But to tell the two subspecies apart, you often need to conduct electrophoresis, requiring the lab scrutiny of the fish's liver. An autopsy.

So far, it appears that Florida bass, and first generation crosses with native bass grow larger than true native bass. Biologists believe Florida bass may live longer than natives. As with most dealings with nature, there are exceptions to this rule, but the average life expectancy for native bass is believed to be 8 to 9 years, while average Florida strain bass may live 12 to 14 years.

At any age, the bass is a marvelous predator, a testament to nature's plan and a key player anywhere it is stocked.

Next, let's look at **CRAPPIE** and see how they live. There are two types of crappie found in private lakes and ponds, the black and the white.

The black crappie is most commonly used in management plans, because it grows larger than a white crappie and it is not quite the prolific spawner as its counterpart.

Black Crappie

Not many know how to tell the two fish apart. Here's the best way: Crappie are identified by counting the hard spines of the dorsal fin (the one on top). If there are less than seven hard spines, the fish is a white crappie. If there are seven or more, it is a black.

The crappie is an active spawner and a predator, so the fish can quickly disrupt the balance in a lake. Most biologists urge pond managers not to stock crappie in bodies of water covering less than 20 acres. Some recommend not using them in lakes that cover

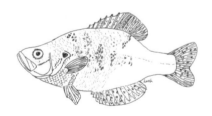

White Crappie

less than 50 acres. These fish tend to overpopulate, then overeat the food chain. Hint: The Texas Parks and Wildlife seldom stocks a new lake with crappie, even if the reservoir has 20,000 surface acres.

As a predator, the crappie stays busy, eating small fish and some large insects. They spawn earlier than other fish in private waters and because of that can quickly disrupt the whole food chain. Their spawning habits are similar to the bass and bluegill. They also make crater-type nests in relatively shallow water.

Most anglers know that the crappie is a very tasty fish, yielding firm white flesh that ranks second only the wall-eye—which is not readily available south of the Mason-Dixon Line—in the author's tastebud test. Even so, introducing crappie to your lake may create management headaches. Exercise caution with this species.

Do you know any catfish anglers? Are you one? If so, you probably have your own secret devices, inventions and love for these whiskered creatures of the night. Two kinds of catfish commonly are stocked in managed waters: Channel cat and blue cat.

These two species have a slippery, skin-like coating on their hides, with no scales. The barbels, or "whiskers," used for sensing the presence of prey in deep, dark waters gives them their feline appearance and name. That legendary catfish angler Huck Finn could tell you that these whiskered species are widely distributed throughout North America, in rivers, ponds, reservoirs and streams.

CHANNEL CATFISH are the most often used, because they are readily available from fish farmers and they readily adapt to less-than-ideal pond environments. If you want to use your private waters to produce food, or if you like to catch your own dinner, the channel cat is your fish.

Channel Catfish

With channel cat, a lake manager can raise upward of 750 to 1,000 pounds per surface acre, more if management techniques are intensified. The same lake will produce only 50 pounds of bass per acre.

Courtesy of Mercury Marine, Fon du Lac, Wisc.

In a small pond, a giant flathead catfish like this 35-pounder can compete with bass for food and present a problem.

Channel catfish reproduce by hiding in a partially closed environment, almost surrounded by their enclosure. Most aquaculturists use barrels, dairy cans or something similar for their channel cat to use in spawning. This is a key point because, without proper nesting habitat, the channel cat will absorb her eggs and not spawn. But given a protected area, when the temperature approaches 72 to 75 degrees, the spawning rituals begin. This is usually after the crappie, bass, bluegill and redear have all spawned in the spring.

The male cleans the nest, then goes find a ripe female and bring her to his abode. The female deposits the eggs, which the male fertilizes and molds into a tidy, compact mass. The male then shoos away the female and stays with the eggs until they hatch and develop enough to leave the nest.

In a pond managed for bass and bluegill, these tiny channel cat are poorly equipped to elude the larger predators. An ice cube probably lasts longer in the water than a catfish fry does once it leaves home on its first and last adventure.

In ponds with catfish only, the spawns often do very

well—sometimes too well. To control their numbers, many lake managers simply deny the channel cat a place to hide, which discourages them from spawning.

The feeding habits of channel cat are that of a teenage boy: They will eat anything. They're both what scientists call opportunistic omnivores, that is, they prefer meat, but will settle for vegetables. In the case of the catfish, this means they'll eat everything from crickets to worms to fathead minnows, whatever is most convenient. The channel catfish is not—repeat, not—a scavenger that makes its living by rooting around in the mud.

In fact, once a channel cat approaches three or four pounds, it becomes an effective predator. In examining the stomach contents of middle-sized catfish, it is not uncommon to find bluegills, crawfish, even small bass in their stomachs. Now you know how these fish grow to be 8 to 12 pounds in a pond.

Key point: They readily accept fish food and are not limited as much by space as the bass. The more pellets you drop in the water, the bigger your catfish will be—to a point. Downside to this comes when the channel cat outgrows its space and creates the potential for a fish-kill by fouling the water with its natural waste.

To avoid this problem, harvest your crop in reasonable and regular fashion. This involves a rod and reel, of course, along with hushpuppies, cole slaw and your favorite beverage.

When it comes to management strategy, the **BLUE CATFISH** comes highly recommended by some, cursed by others. If you know about this fish, you can make a good decision based on your goals.

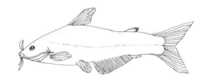

Blue Catfish

First, the blue cat grows to weights exceeding 100 pounds in large waters. Private lakes smaller than 50 acres have yielded blue cats weighing 50 pounds.

This fish is dark gray or blue in color, carries a forked tail and features a slight rise just in front of the dorsal fin, thus its nickname of humpback blue or high-fin blue.

Its lifestyle contrasts with that of the channel cat from spawning to feeding to where they live.

When stocked together, a channel will outgrow a blue for the first two years. After that, however, the blue puts on a growth spurt and overtakes the fast-starting channel. Blues eat fish and other live creatures, but can be conditioned to take a commercial pellet ration.

Blues tend not to spawn well consistently until they are 6 to 10 pounds. If you plan to stock blue cat, be ready to deal with their very large sizes. A 30-pound blue will give far less respect to your prized four-pound bass than you do.

For some lakes, the thoughtful manager may want to consider using shad. This species of baitfish is sometimes used in bass-bluegill lakes, especially if the manager is interested in growing trophy-size bass.

In the U.S., shad come in two main varieties, the **GIZZARD SHAD** and the **THREADFIN**.

The gizzard shad is common throughout North

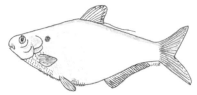

Gizzard Shad

America, occupying most every large watershed in the South and Southwest. Ironically, most every public lake and river contains a gizzard shad population, but it exists in private waters only if it is stocked or if a lake has caught runoff from another water source.

Gizzard shad provide good news and bad news for the pond manager. Yes, they achieve great size, growing to 16 to 18 inches in length and weighing more than two pounds. Trouble is, they reach these proportions so quickly, the bass and other predators cannot keep pace. The bass are outgrown by their food source. The gizzard shad population, without a natural enemy, could grow out of control.

Fortunately, Mother Nature has a way of keeping this fish in check. Once the gizzard shad reaches a high population density, the fish naturally stops spawning.

Gizzard shad lay thousands of eggs on grass and grass-type vegetation under the water, early in the morning during spring months, just as shiners do. Only difference is that shad spawn at a slightly lower temperature than shiners, 68 to 72 degrees. A full-grown gizzard shad may carry more than 80,000 eggs.

One thing to remember about nature is that parental care has a direct impact on how many eggs a fish will lay. The more a parent takes care of its eggs, the fewer eggs are laid. Nature's goal is to replace the parents, that's all. Gizzard shad—and threadfins, for that matter—just lay their eggs and take off. Good bye, good luck.

Gizzard shad are primarily filter feeders, always in a school, but they will root around on the bottom, stirring up food. They can be identified, compared to threadfins, by looking at their mouths: Gizzards have a nose, that is their mouth is on the underside of the face that opens somewhat downward. This fish is long, silver in color, with silver-colored fins. A threadfin is much smaller, growing to seven inches, with a mouth at the end of its face that opens more upward. The threadfin features yellowish, or golden-colored fins.

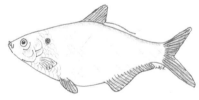

Threadfin Shad

Both shad species congregate in thick schools of similar size, preferring open water to structure. Since they are small fish, the schooling affords them protection from bigger fish. Once a big predator sees the school he is often confused because he can't pick out just one. True, the predator may get its meal, but the school can get away with most members intact.

Die-offs of large gizzard shad are common, especially in waters where the population has stopped reproducing. These die-offs typically occur during cooler months and the weakest fish are thinned out by nature. This may be nature's way of correcting overpopulation of shad that are too large.

The threadfin shad is quite a bit different than the gizzard in that threadfins cannot tolerate low temperatures, period. Once your lake reaches and stays below 42 degrees Fahrenheit, even for short periods—such as overnight—threadfins die.

The threadfin shad is wonderful fish to use to grow large bass, as long as you can manage the temperature problems. Threadfins feed by filtering plankton from the water and do not root around on the bottom as gizzards do. But with the threadfin, availability is often a question. Even veteran fish farmers find the threadfin to be vulnerable to temperature change and excess handling.

Another fish to consider is not a species at all, but rather, a man-made cross between a male striped bass and a female white bass (sand bass). Meet the **HYBRID STRIPER**, or wiper as it's often called in the Midwest.

These fish are artificially spawned in hatcheries where the eggs are stripped from the female, fertilized with the creamy milt of the males, then placed in jars with fresh running water. At just the right temperature and chemistry, they are hatched and then stocked as small fry into fertile ponds. These laboratory creations are conditioned to eat artificial feeds and are fed virtually round the clock. These fish are added to the management mix to add diversity to a pond or used when a lake will not support the species more commonly used.

These fish are eating machines and grow rapidly. Reportedly, pond owners have stocked hybrid fingerlings and caught six-pounders a year later! What's more, these fish can be fed commercial pellets to allow a standing crop of hundreds of pounds per acre.

This feature makes the hybrid striper a fine "eraser," a fish used to thin out a particular type of fish that has become overstocked. Because the hybrid can not reproduce, the manager retains firm control over its numbers.

The hybrid reaches weights up to 20 pounds, sometimes more in large public reservoirs with a heavy forage base. The hybrid striper readily strikes lures and once hooked, it pulls with the speed of a bass and the strength of a striper. Great stuff.

There is still much to learn about these fish, especially the way they interrelate with other fish. Little is known about how largemouth bass live with them, the impact they have on the natural food chain, even considering the fact that most of them are fed artificial feed most of their lives. Most people who raise them, however, have noted a need for shad with hybrid stripers.

At this point, the primary role of this fish is to give a lake owner or manager a "three-car garage" rather than a two, just to have something no one else has, or to correct an otherwise uncorrectable situation. Commercial producers in the Carolinas, Arkansas, Mississippi and Texas have developed steady markets to the restaurant trade in Japan, Southeast Asia and Europe.

When trying to manage vegetation, one option you have are **GRASS CARP**, also called **WHITE AMUR**. Some states allow diploid grass carp, a fish that reproduces in the wild. Many states, including Texas, allow only the sterile triploid.

Both fish have a streamlined body shape with large scales, usually olive green or creamy in color. "Old Rubber Lips" has a soft, fleshy mouth, on the front of its head that allows the fish to eat vegetation above its body or to cruise the bottom, feeding on rooted plants.

The cigar-shaped fish may eat its own body weight in milfoil, hydrilla or other vegetation every day. In small ponds they may reach 10 pounds in as many months, topping out at 50 pounds. In larger private lakes of five acres or more, grass carp may be a good fish to consider.

Diploid grass carp are White Amur that develop eggs and can be fertilized. The natural range of this fish is in the eastern and central part of Asia, where it exists in rivers and streams. There is documentation that small diploid grass carp have been found in the Mississippi River watershed, suggesting they may be spawning in public waters. So far, there seems to be no evidence of reproduction anywhere else, but there is evidence the fish have escaped into rivers, lakes and streams.

These two fish have been the subject of much controversy, generating fear and loathing among bass clubbers and contradictory research by scientists. But professionals who have used them have developed confidence in the grass carp's ability to safely control vegetation.

Grass Carp

On this everyone agrees: If overstocked, the fish will eat all submersed vegetation in a lake. This could prove to be a political problem in large public lakes—and already has in some states—but this is an issue of fishing tactics, not necessarily management techniques. The bass , striper and crappie still remain in the lake. The angler must look for them in different areas than before.

Biological problems occur, however, where vegetation is needed to harbor young-of-the-year animals such as shrimp or larval salt water fish. It is a problem in wetlands, where the vegetation is needed for food for aquatic animals as well as migratory birds. Migratory birds need this shallow-water vegetation to hide their nests and young birds.

Grass carp eat submersed vegetation, or commercial fish pellets, if presented regularly. The triploid version has been genetically altered to sterilize it. This prevents even the most remote chance of reproduction.

Many states require on-site inspection by a U.S. Fish and Wildlife biologist to certify as sterile every triploid carp released from an accredited fish farm. State and federal laws dictate the wise and prudent use of the grass carp. Check with local authorities before stocking this fish.

Most common trash fish found in private waters are
GAR and the **COMMON CARP**, also called the German carp. These fish are active spawners, with the female laying 100,000 eggs in a single nest. No wonder these fish can turn a sizable body of water into a glorified mud hole, as thousands of carp root along the lake bottom, disturbing the sediment, scavenging for food. Many large public lakes in the U.S. carry a large standing crop of carp, often taking up more space than all other fish combined. Imagine the problems a few can do in a smallish private impoundment.

The **BUFFALOFISH** is another species of limited value in private waters. This fish is built along similar lines as the common carp, but feeds more on small minnows, rather than carrion and vegetation.

Gar are also found in private lakes. As a top-line predator, this toothy creature competes directly against your gamefish for food. In fact, with a 10-pound gar, the smaller bass may themselves become a food source. The remedy is to remove the primitive looking gar.

These unwelcome visitors usually find themselves in private lakes when rivers or nearby lakes overflow their normal confines.

Other fish of questionable value include the green sunfish and the warmouth, often called goggle-eye or rock bass. By any name, these species compete with young bass for food and space, while providing little recreation or protein at the bottom of the food chain.

Stocking Strategies

Decide what you hope to get from your pond: Food or fun? Fillets or trophy fish? Maybe you want to raise catfish and bluegill to eat after church on Sundays. Producing trophy largemouth for catch-and-release recreation may be your goal.

In any case, you want your fish-stocking program to fit your goals as closely as possible. Otherwise, you end up with a polka-dot fish population living in a plaid lake. Polka-dots and plaid. They don't match.

Say, for instance, you have a 1/2-acre pond and want to grow trophy bass. You face far more limitations (and the potential for failure) than someone with a 20-acre lake. Without spending money like an oil sheik on shad, crawfish and other food to feed your bass, it simply cannot be done.

At every turn, factor in the limitations you may encounter with the size and water quality of your lake. What kind of operating budget can you afford?

Simply put, the size of your lake has a direct influence on what you can or cannot do, simply based on the amount of food the tiny system can produce for your bass. The clarity of the water has a direct impact on what can happen. The geographic location of the lake also will determine what you can do. Geography and elevation determine the length of your growing season—

For recreation, most pond managers use largemouth bass as the featured predator.

for backyard tomato plants, for fish, for everything.

As a rule, the smaller a body of water, the easier to manage. You can make wholesale changes more easily and with less cost than with a big lake. But there are limits to what you can grow in a small pond.

Biologists concur that ponds of less than one surface acre in the South are most conducive to growing channel catfish— up to several hundred pounds of fish per acre of water, with fathead minnows as a natural food source and supplementary feeding of a commercial ration. Some biologists also recommend stocking hybrid sunfish or the hybrid striper, sometimes called the wiper (cross between a white bass and a striper), to provide another type of fish to be caught.

No reservoir can produce good fishing without a strong foundation at the base of the food chain.

But the nation's leading authorities generally agree that in waters smaller than one acre, forget about producing much of a large bass population, unless you want to spend hundreds of dollars to provide live forage.

The channel catfish is widely used in stocking private waters, for a variety of reasons. The species is readily available from fish farmers at competitive prices and it's relatively easy to grow because they will eat commercial feed.

The fathead minnow complements the catfish because they live in a different niche in the environment and do not compete. At the same time fatheads reproduce heavily during the warm months and provide catfish with additional natural food during the year.

The hybrid sunfish doesn't appear to be the light-tackle buster that would grow to two pounds, as biologists thought it might back in the late-1970s. Full-grown, the fish will typically weigh less than 1/2 pound and the fish, although hybrid, have a tendency to reproduce just enough to be a headache to a manager. When they do reproduce, they cannot physically be what their parents are, because they are "backcrosses," inferior to their parents.

As a sight feeder, the largemouth needs fairly clear water to realize its full potential.

Stock largemouth bass only with the knowledge that this fish stands directly at the top of the food chain, typically eating much of the available baitfish in a small pond. Then you wind up with just a few nice bass and are faced with not being able to harvest very many so as to not compromise the delicate balance of the food chain.

Clarity of the water may influence your stocking decision. For example, channel catfish do not have to see to eat. Their whiskers have "tastebuds" on them that allow this fish to forage around and taste things before they even eat. Some sunfish, such as bluegill, are aggressive enough to attack movement in the water, eating something before they even know what it is. If they don't like it, they spit it out.

A bass, on the other hand, is a "sight-feeder," relying mostly on the eyes to identify its prey. Ponds with chronic low visibility—especially when related to suspended solids (muddy water)—should only be stocked with channel catfish or those fish, such as the fathead minnow, that can interrelate with channel catfish.

Ponds larger than one acre allow a little more management flexibility if you want to raise largemouth bass, especially if the visibility is greater than 10 or 12 inches.

Got all that?

Just to make sure, let's think our way through a typical new pond or renovation project.

Meet our good friend Joe. His new 16-acre pond has just filled in the past year, it's holding water and he has decided to stock it with fish.

Joe would like to manage for channel catfish, bass, bluegill and fathead minnows. Business is going well, so he hopes to retire in five years, move to this weekend haven where he and his wife can watch wildlife, take their morning walks and entertain the grandkids.

In Joe's mind, he sees his youngest granddaughter, now four years old, learning to bait her own hook with an earthworm and catching a bucket full of bream. He sees his wife and the oldest grandchild, now 12, out in the boat with grins stretching from bow to stern, youngster's rod bent double under the pressure of a bass bigger than he has ever seen.

Joe really knows what he wants. How does he get there?

If Joe's smart—and he is—he will study the stocking rates recommended by his state game and fish commission and, when the time is right, purchase the right number of bait species to support the bass and other predators he stocks.

Recommended stocking rates vary, but the Texas Chapter of the American Fisheries Society suggests stocking fathead minnows and bluegill first, along with channel cat, then waiting at least six months before stocking largemouth bass fingerlings.

This builds the food chain from the bottom up. The general formula is four pounds of fathead minnows per surface acre of pond, 200 channel catfish and 1,000 bluegill per acre.

Joe has heard from a consulting biologist that coppernose bluegill may reach almost two pounds south of the Mason-Dixon Line so, just for fun, he decides to use them. He knows he could stock channel cat at a high rate, especially if he wants to feed them with commercial pellets, but at 200 per acre, he could add more cats later.

Joe could have gone for the quick fix, stocking his lake to provide immediate action—50 pounds of fathead minnows and 2,000 bluegill to feed 20 bass 8- to 16-inches long per acre. With catchable size bass in the lake, he and his family could be catching these aggressive predators on spinners in a matter of weeks.

It also would have been expensive. And Joe's got more

time than he does money. So he's sticking to his original timetable and budget, and letting Mother Nature put size on his bass.

With stocking season—summer—just around the corner, Joe begins to contact hatcheries that could provide his fish. After shopping for price and quality, Joe gets comfortable with his fish supplier, he finalizes the early stages of his stocking schedule.

June or July arrives, and the whole gang is gathered at lakeside to witness the big event. Gently, Joe's wife and family carry buckets full of tiny fingerlings to the water's edge and release them.

Joe's buddies snap pictures and run a camcorder to record the moment for posterity. And why not? This is a major event. In two years, with proper management, the tiny fish going in today will put a bend in Joe's granddaughter's rod—and a smile on her face.

While we wait for Joe's fish to grow, maybe we should just go back over the basics. Need a quick review?

For small, muddy ponds, stock with channel catfish and fathead minnows for their food. In clear, deep, large lakes, stock with largemouth bass, using bluegill for their forage base.

For basic advice on stocking your pond, follow this key:

DECISION	NEXT STEP
1. Pond size	
A. Less than 1 acre	*Go to 2*
B. Greater than 1 acre	*Go to 3*
2. Ponds less than 1 acre	
A. Fish not fed consistently stock 100 channel catfish and 4 pounds of fatheads	*Go to 13*
B. Fish fed consistently, at least 4 times weekly stock up to 1,000 catfish and 6 pounds of fatheads	*STOP*

            C. Bass, bluegill desired   *See biologist*

3. Ponds greater than 1 acre
    A. pond muddy (<10" visibility)   *Go to 4*
    B. pond clear (>10" visibility)   *Go to 5*
4. Pond muddy
    A. Want to clear it up? Consult biologist   *Go to 5*
    B. Leave it as is
        (1) stock 4 pounds of fatheads (and)
        (2) stock 500 bluegill fingerlings per acre   *Go to 10*
        (or)
        (3) stock 250 bluegill and   *Go to 10*
        250 redear fingerlings per acre
        (or)
        (4) stock 75 adult bluegill/acre (>3")   *Go to 10*
        (and optionally)
        (5) 500 golden shiners per acre

5. Pond clear
    A. Water acidic—pH less than 7   *Go to 6*
    B. Water alkaline—pH greater than 7   *Go to 7*

6. Pond acid — typically pine forest areas
    A. Stock 250 bluegill fingerlings   *Go to 10*
        and 250 redear fingerlings (1-3")
        (or)
    B. Stock 50 bluegill adults   *Go to 10*
        and 25 redear adults (>3")

7. Pond alkaline — How much rain do you get?
    A. Fewer than 20 inches yearly   *Go to 8*
    B. More than 20 inches yearly   *Go to 9*

8. Fewer than 20 inches of rain yearly
    A. Stock 500 bluegill fingerlings;   *Go to 10*
        4 pounds of fatheads; and 500 golden
        shiners/acre. (or)
    B. Stock 75 adult bluegill   *Go to 10*
        and 500 large golden shiners per acre.

9. More than 20 inches of rain yearly
    A. Stock 500 bluegill fingerlings
        and 4 pounds of fathead minnows/acre. *Go to 10*
        (or)

B. Stock 75 adult bluegills/acre *Go to 10*
   (and optional)
C. Stock 500 shiners/acre

10. Want channel catfish, also?
A. If not fed, stock 100 *Go to 11*
B. If fed consistently, stock up to 1,000 *Go to 11*
C. Don't want catfish? *Go to 11*

11. Timetable for stocking fish.
A. Stock fingerling sunfish and other
   forage fish any time except hottest and
   coldest months. Stock fingerling bass
   after spring spawns.
B. Stock advanced sunfish and advanced
   bass at the same time in spring, or stock
   adult sunfish in fall and fingerling bass
   in spring.
C. Stock catfish, at least as large as the bass *Go to 12*
   you intend to stock, at the same time
   forage fish are stocked.

12. Stocking bass
A. If fingerlings, stock between 50-100/acre *Go to 13*
B. If advanced, stock no more than 20/acre *Go to 13*

13. Fertilization program?
If you fertilize regularly, double your *STOP*
forage fish and unfed catfish stocking
rates, leave bass and fed catfish rates as is.

(*Pond Boss* tip: This key allows for flexibility. Stock your
predator fish only after forage has been established. Depending on your goals, you may choose to stock other fish such as
threadfin shad, blue catfish or hybrid stripers.)

Controlling
the Harvest

Stop me if you've heard this story before but...Your friend describes a trip he just took to a good-looking fishing hole that appeared to have everything—fertile water, lots of gamefish habitat, pleasant surroundings, fish stocked by the score.

But the fishing stank.

Your friend (or maybe this is you) fished for hours without much success. True, fishing is fishing and no trip comes with a written guarantee, but seldom have you fished a lake that held more promise, yet delivered so little.

How many times have you heard about a lake that has been "fished out?" Or the pond is full of fish, but they're all too small?

These are two of the chief complaints, along with runaway vegetation, I get from pond managers. When I survey the lake in question, I find the fish population to be totally out of balance, generally due to improper harvest. Anglers have taken too many fish from the system or, in many cases, they have taken too few.

Either way, there is a

Through selective harvest, the lake manager can promote high-quality fishing. Often, small ponds are overrun with stunted crappie, but this fine specimen is the exception.

problem that can be corrected with proper harvest. Better, these conditions can be prevented. And it all starts with the guy on the business end of the rod and reel. The decisions he or she makes—which fish to keep and how many—become the important management tools you've got after the lake is stocked.

Basically, harvest of fish follows the principles of crop harvest. A ranch manager knows his range land will hold only a given number of cattle per acre without overtaxing the environment. He knows that if the cattle overgraze the grasses, the animals will deteriorate, right along with the land itself. A gardener knows that pinching off blooms from tomato plants stimulates the growth of the remaining blossoms. Similar principles apply to your fish.

Consider yourself a water farmer or rancher, with fish as your main crop. You wouldn't run a stripper through your cotton patch while the plants were still in the boll stage would you? Of course not. You would wait until the plants had fully developed. You should do the same with your fish. With apologies to the TV commercial...harvest no fish before its time.

This is where selective

This photo from the 1970s shows what a healthy lake can produce, but imagine the impact of removing this many adult-size bass from the fishery.

harvest comes in. Selective harvest. It's the taking of fish from your lake, all right, but only with some thought beforehand.

In a new pond, the strategy should be simple: Do not take any fish the first year.

Give all your fish the opportunity to spawn at least once. After your fish have this running start, in most healthy waters, you will be ready to implement your plans.

Perhaps your goal is to maintain bass in a balanced fishery. In that case, you will want to harvest bass in all size ranges.

In a *Pond Boss* How-To Book on raising trophy largemouth, we dig deeper into bass management, but for now, go with this general rule: You may harvest up to 25, maybe even 35, pounds of bass per acre per year. Notice the "up to." Twenty-five pounds may seem like a lot, until you consider that it's only a handful of five-pound bass in a 12-month period.

A tight bag limit? Yes. But in order to develop and maintain a healthy fishery in full balance, you'll have to set the limit and educate your friends and family to help you enforce it. Nothing wrong with catching dozens of bass, as long as you release all but the magic 25 pounds per acre.

A simple guideline for lake managers is to use a self-imposed minimum length limit for the second and third years, then adjust it upward after that.

For example, during the second and third years the minimum length may be 14 inches, moved to 16 inches during the fourth. People develop their trophy bass by taking out some of their yearling bass and by removing a few

To produce trophy bass, the pond boss may need to restrict the harvest of largemouth with tight bag limits

older fish. This practice of removing fish under 14 inches and over 21 inches, for example, is known as slot limit, which eliminates much of the competition for food.

If you hope to develop a bass fishery, never forget that your star attraction is an aggressive predator and, as such, may be easily caught. There is a threat of overharvest of bass, especially in small ponds, so it is important to not allow large numbers to be harvested in short periods of time. Better, harvest these fish over the course of a full season. On the other hand, underharvest of bass can present problems, too.

A well-managed bass/bluegill population will grow and maintain 80 pounds of bass per acre. The average managed pond will have around 50 to 60 pounds per acre. We also know that it typically takes five pounds of baitfish for a bass to gain a pound. So, your pond must produce a significant amount of forage at the bottom of the food chain, primarily bluegill, to put weight on your bass.

This means that, over time, it's a good idea to remove a few large bluegill. One splendid fishery in Georgia has managed its private waters to the point that a nationally known angler films an occasional TV show there, using four-pound line to catch sunfish weighing up to two pounds.

Many states recommend removing 4 to 6 pounds of sunfish from your pond for every pound of bass you harvest.

Bonus benefit: Harvesting large sunfish stimulates those left to spawn, keeping the food chain active and dynamic.

How do you know which bass to remove? It's like going through a forest of old-growth trees, marking a few to be removed for the common good.

To that end, use a catch-record form to keep track of how many bass are caught, released or taken. If you catch a fish, measure its length and weigh it on portable scales. This will help you monitor the growth of your fish population as it matures.

It will also indicate if your fish are getting everything they need. The game commission in your state has developed standards of length/weight ratios for various fish species. A 14-inch bass in Texas, for instance, should weigh 1.6 pounds, according to Texas Parks and Wildlife surveys. Check your catch records. As long as your fish are growing at acceptable rates posted by your state, your management plan is working. Don't fix it. It ain't broke.

At some point, a particular size range of fish may begin to dominate the catch-record charts. As this occurs, you will likely see the weights on these fish decline. Say our 14-inch bass is weighing 14 ounces instead of 1.6 pounds. That's an indication of overcrowding. Remember underharvest being a problem? That could be the culprit here.

In the introduction, you read about a group of South Texas landowners with a 50-acre lake and a problem with overpopulated, stunted bass.

After evaluation, I encouraged them to stock 1,500 adult bluegill sunfish that could start a new forage base right away and urged them to harvest every bass measuring less than 14 inches long. Somebody asked how many fish to remove.

That decision came from catch records. The log would tell the landowners when the fishery was back in balance and the bass were growing again. This particular lake was so badly overrun with bass, it took several years to show proper length/weight ratios. Once balance was regained, it was, and remains, an excellent fishery.

R ealize, though, that managing for bass and managing for trophy bass are two different strategies. Similar but different.

The keys for raising giant largemouth lie in the food chain and in harvest of the fish. Lots of one, precious little of the other.

You don't have to make an A in fisheries biology 101 to know that a 6-pound bass will not grow in the skillet! Basically, you manage for trophy bass by protecting the large fish and harvesting the small ones. Always release the largest bass and remove the smaller ones. Doing this, you will reduce the number of bass, while preserving the largest of the group. Look at it this way—if your lake can grow 60 pounds of bass per acre, how many 10-pound bass will it support? Six. Only six. Any more than that exceeds the carrying capacity of the water.

L et's take a look at harvest from another standpoint. When you take large numbers of fish from a lake, what happens to the remaining fish? They have more room, more food, so they spawn even more vigorously than before.

So your job is never done. The advantage you end up with is larger fish that can help you harvest some of the smaller bass as food. It is that same principle that is an asset when it comes to baitfish.

Consider harvesting other fish species, too. Channel catfish, especially those fed a commercial ration, need to be harvested. Channel cat have a bad habit of outgrowing their environment, especially if they have food available.

One of the most common problems a biologist comes across is the over-fed, underharvested catfish pond. When the call for help comes in, it is usually too late to prevent the catfish from getting sick or dying, due to poor water quality.

If you choose to stock larger numbers of catfish, harvest them sooner, and in larger numbers. Catfish on supplementary feed will flourish from fingerlings to 1 1/2 pounds in a single year, taking up more space in their environment as they grow.

For that reason, I encourage my clients to view their catfish as a put-and-take fishery. Food on the fin. Stock them, grow them, catch them, eat them. Then restock.

One of the special joys of raising channel catfish comes in the harvest.

See, even when your catfish are headed for the table, harvest stands as a dominant theme in your management strategy. Learn the basic principles of selective harvest, develop catch records and use them consistently. Before your very eyes, your efforts will begin to bear fruit. You will study your length/weight charts and see that, yes, your 12-inch bass are putting on weight.

Most importantly, you will realize that the fish you remove from your lake may be just as important as those you leave in it.

"Do not tell fish stories where the people know you; but particularly, don't tell them where they know fish."
—*Mark Twain*

Habitat Management

Gamefish habitat and cover may be brush piles, rocks—even your fishing pier.

Few concepts in lake management are more widely misunderstood than fish habitat. It seems simple enough. An old tree standing naked in the water. An underwater ditch. It's all habitat, right?

Maybe so, maybe no.

Ironically, even as sportfishermen get more skilled and knowledgeable, the information gap on gamefish habitat and the terms "structure" and "habitat" seems to grow wider every year.

Before we tie ourselves in a knot here, let's define "habitat." Simple. It's the environment a species needs to live, reproduce and raise its young.

On the other hand, "cover," a term we all see in the popular fishing magazines, is something altogether different. Biologically speaking, the term translates to a feature, usually located on the lake bottom—log jam, rock pile or standing timber—that fish use as a social gathering place. To the fish, it's rather like home base.

See the kicker? Many sportfishermen think cover is vital to a lake's ability to support fish. They also think cover is critical for spawning. Not true.

If cover were important to producing fish, commercial fish farms would be the first to use it, yet the typical fish farm pond is totally barren of anything that would invite the hopeful cast of a fisherman. Cover, then, is what fishermen look for when trying to catch their favorite gamefish.

The fathead minnow, for instance, feeds on plankton and insects, basically in shallow water, and spawns on flooded rocks, boards or tires. The hybrid striper needs deeper, more open, water. Largemouth bass spawn in gravel beds, feed around cover where baitfish congregate. The channel catfish can tolerate shallow, warm water with low oxygen content, but it needs flooded drain pipes or other hollowed-out hiding places to spawn.

Understanding the different needs of these species will help you design the proper habitat for the fish your stock in your lake.

O nce you have planned a suitable environment for your gamefish, and they get established, you may want to add cover to make the fish more available to rod-and-reelers. For obvious reasons, it's easier to add structure before your lake has filled. Ask your buddies to help move tire reefs, Christmas trees and other cover by boat one icy winter day, and you may be testing those friendships.

Some pond managers have improved fishing by building artificial cover from old car tires.

In my consulting work, I'm often asked what kind of cover works best. After surveying the lake and analyzing it, I usually suggest a so-called "permanent" cover. By permanent, I mean that it doesn't grow. Ridges, cliffs, drop-offs fall into this category. So do rock piles, tire reefs, pipes, concrete blocks and hardwood trees.

Over time, I have found that pond owners get more maintenance-free recreation out of an inert object than from introducing a live plant that may grow out of control.

It's crucial to place this new cover in the proper area of the lake.

In the South, the lake manager will be best-served by placing the cover in shallow water, typically less than 10 feet below the surface. The smaller the impoundment, the shallower your cover needs to be.

Conversely, the larger your lake, the deeper you can have cover.

Here's why: In the summer months, your lake will stratify, like a layer cake, with the cooler bands of water sinking to the bottom, the warmer layers rising. A "thermocline" develops.

Remember, when you were a kid swimming in a pond during the summer? Your feet were cold, but your chest was warm? Or you may have dived down and felt that cold water? You penetrated the thermocline, that layer of water that has become basically stagnant, void of oxygen.

Fish cannot survive below the thermocline for very long, of course, and they will not congregate below those depths.

The size of your lake, wind action, clarity of the water, inflow, air temperature—all these factors determine the depth of the thermocline. Regardless of the depth, you have wasted time, money and sweat if you built a tire reef and sank it below this depth.

Brush is the most common structure that winds up at the bottom of private lakes and ponds. To improve their fishing success, pond owners will collect willow limbs, discarded trees—any woody-type vegetation that's readily available yet small enough to handle—and gather it into stacks or piles.

In building your brush piles, think fluffy. For some reason, bass and crappie seem to prefer thin, limber branches over the main trunk of a large tree. In my survey work through the years, I've noticed that if a tree has enough small branches, the gamefish will hide in them, waiting to ambush their prey, making trails through the limbs.

To be most effective, your brush should be gathered together, yes, but in a rather loose configuration to allow fish to move freely in and out of the fish hotel. Compacted piles are not nearly as effective.

"Now that I've worn out a chain saw in gathering this brush, where do I set my fish cover?" That's a question I often get asked at lake management seminars and consulting sessions, and my answer may differ from that of other fisheries biologists.

I like to see fish cover placed in shallow water, especially in lakes south of the Mason-Dixon Line where summer stratification gets to be a problem. Shallow?

Try to set the piles where the top is less than four feet from the surface of the water, and the rest spreads out to the bottom of the lake. In a one-acre pond, pick five or 10 spots that provide easy access for fishermen and position your brush in piles 10 feet by 10 feet.

If you choose to use Christmas trees, bind them loosely together with baling twine or similar material, not wire, then tie a concrete block rather loosely to the group and sink this in a spot convenient to anglers.

As you build these brush piles, you may discover that six or seven average-size trees make quite a bundle. Work with a half-dozen trees at a time. Any more, and you've signed on for a wrestling match.

Some folks go to the trouble of buying plastic buckets,

placing the tree in the bucket and filling the bucket with concrete. Then they carefully sink the thing so that the tree stands upright on the bottom. Fish love it, but this gets into work. Most consultants don't encourage the cement/bucket routine simply because bundles or piles have improved fishing success in private lakes from Michigan to Alabama, with fewer allergic reactions to manual labor.

Unfortunately, Christmas trees may have the shortest life of any new cover you could introduce to your pond. Trees are natural, organic, biodegradable, environmentally correct. Alas, they're also temporary.

Softwood trees typically deteriorate to the point that they become ineffective and need replacing after four or five years under water. The small limbs decompose, leaving only the trunk.

Also, pines and evergreens used as Christmas trees go through a decomposition process that produces toxic gases, usually hydrogen sulfide (smells like rotten eggs. Lovely.). In sufficient quantities, these gases may cause problems with fish and other forms of aquatic life.

If your lake is in an area known to be acidic, put your trees out in intervals, a few stacks in January and a few more in April, not all at once. A gradual program helps insure the least disruption of your lake environment.

If you are putting cover in an old lake, consider the water may suffer from the addition of organic cover. Ask your consultant.

Consider using rock piles as shallow-water fish attractors. They can be very effective, especially for channel catfish, bluegill and redear sunfish, if the rocks are placed near a flooded creek channel or drop-off.

In this case, bigger is better. Larger rocks make better fish attractors. But watch that bad back, Hercules. For hauling and stacking any boulder heavier than your tackle box, call your buddies, Kubota and John Deere, and ask them to show up at your pond with the front-end loaders.

Concrete blocks, often called "cinder blocks," also make an effective artificial reef, but two or three scattered blocks serve no purpose. They need to cover a considerable area—10

Illustration courtesy of Randy Mack Bishop, Dallas, Texas

Many pond managers improve their fishery by adding cinder blocks, Christmas trees and other bottom structure. Place these objects at varying depths.

feet by 10 feet by four feet high—to be most effective.

Blocks are readily available and easy to stack and haul. Fish move in and out of the blocks with an apparent sense of security. But keep your wallet handy. These blocks cost $1, maybe $1.50 apiece, so a functional reef may cost $40-$75.

Old tires can make a practical reef. I have found that tires are best used in ponds where other cover is also available. By themselves, tires won't produce the fishing results you could expect from a lake with varied structure.

For best results, bind the tires together, three at time, sidewall to sidewall, in the shape of a triangle, then put several together to form a pyramid. Be sure each tire has a hole drilled in the "top" to allow air to escape. Otherwise, they may float. Now that sight makes a beautiful addition to the aesthetics.

You might also try stacking pipes made of metal, tile or PVC and sinking them for gamefish cover.

Here again, bigger is better. The larger the pipe diameter, the more effective it can be.

Sewer pipe, especially in lengths of 4 to 8 feet, gives catfish a harbor for spawning and provides bass and bluegill the gathering place they seem to like. PVC pipe makes excellent cover when coupled together in "tree" shapes. With PVC pipes, anglers are less likely to lose their lures on snags.

When it comes to developing new cover, I've seen lake managers use barrels, cans, even old refrigerators. These metal objects provide hollowed-out spaces attractive to channel and blue catfish in spawning, but raise potential hazards with toxic chemicals. Refrigerators may still have oil and freon and other gook in their compressors and coils, so beware of these fish-killers. And if aesthetics are important, a rusty Kenmore sitting in the mud in times of low water doesn't look so hot either.

In many ponds, habitat and structure management means focusing attention on the natural, green, growing variety—moss, weeds, aquatic vegetation.

Call it what you like. It's common to most North American waters and a key factor in the environment of any private lake or pond. But controlling vegetation when it becomes too much of a good thing can stir up controversy right quick, especially between biologists and fishermen.

Anglers love aquatic vegetation because bass and other species use it for hiding and seeking shelter from sun. This gives fishermen "hot spots" where they can concentrate on casting to visible targets. Makes fishing more fun.

But for the lake manager, this gamefish cover can become a headache. Vegetation grows. It recedes. It grows some more.

Trouble is, once vegetation covers more than 15 to 20 percent of the lake, it becomes a nuisance. Mats of vegetation tangle your fishing lure, block boating and swimming, tie up nutrients in the water and disperse fish, instead of concentrating them.

The practical lake manager plans vegetation even before

the pond is ever built.

Vegetation must have three things: soil nutrients, the right temperature and sunlight. Obviously, we have little control over temperature and nutrient content, but we can make sure the sunlight doesn't penetrate to the bottom.

In North America, unwanted vegetation is most likely to grow in water less than three feet deep. Solve your vegetation problems before they begin by constructing your lake to eliminate shallow water.

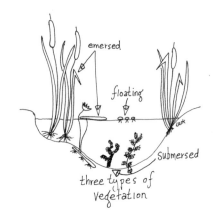

Aquatic vegetation comes in three basic varieties—submersed, emersed and floating. All have a useful function in a healthy reservoir.

Thousands of American lake managers never had the chance to design a lake from scratch. We usually have ponds built by others, which means we either let vegetation problems develop or inherited them outright.

For many, then, the vegetation becomes a question of identifying the good plants from the bad guys and controlling the bad ones.

Unfortunately, lake managers often pick the wrong method of control and get no results. Frustration quickly sets in and the novice pond boss looks for a quick fix by violating the prescribed doses of chemicals. The stage is set for a miniature environmental disaster, right in your lake.

Stop this cycle before it starts.

Learn the soil-based plants—so-called "emergants" such as cattails, bulrushes, lotus, smartweed and lily pads—from the submersed species, those that grow under water—algae, pondweeds, milfoil and coontail. Some floating plants such as duckweed and watermeal can present problems, too.

Only by recognizing your vegetation can you make wise decisions in checking its growth. Control methods vary.

In the winter, lowering the water level in a pond will help control aquatic vegetation around the shoreline.

Physical control is least expensive. It involves pulling the unwanted vegetation by hand or chopping it with a tool or machine and hauling it off. It can be sweaty work.

Many designs of underwater mowers have been developed. Some actually provide temporary relief. Other contraptions have failed miserably. If a commercial firm offers to run a weed-eating machine through your pond, ask for references. Better yet, ask how long you can expect control once you have written him the check. The yellow flag's up...caution.

"Drawdown" remains the most practical physical management. By draining enough water from the lake to expose vegetation to the air, you use Mother Nature's freezing temperatures to throttle its growth.

This is usually done in the late autumn or early winter, prior to icing or early-spring rains. Old Man Winter knocks down the weeds, then, once the lake refills with spring rains, vegetation is under control. Trouble is, some geographical areas need the water more than they need vegetation control in this way. They cannot afford the luxury of releasing water, just to improve fishing.

Biological control uses plants or animals, or even insects, to manage vegetation.

These days, the white amur (grass carp) provides one of the most natural controls we have. But laws on using this fish vary from state to state.

This controversial fish has been accused of overeating its food supply and disrupting the environment, most notably the bass population. Thus, it has become a political hot potato in some states, especially Texas, where it was once stocked in grossly exaggerated numbers of adult fish and did not control the hydrilla mats at Lake Conroe, north of Houston. These overstocked grass carp wiped out virtually anything green. Grass carp didn't eat any bass, understand, they just left the bass clubbers short of visible casting targets. The anglers were forced to find bass in deep water, where their fishing skills are not nearly so proficient.

Political football.

Anglers coast-to-coast worry about grass carp reproducing their own kind, taking over the vegetation. There has been documentation of juvenile grass carp in the Mississippi River watershed, indicating that reproduction in the environment.

Meanwhile, fisheries specialists see the fish as a management tool, a way to reduce the use of harsh chemicals.

In between, state and federal agencies search for a means of using white amur, without its dominating a fishery. So far, the so-called triploid, or sterile grass carp, seems to be the middle ground.

For guidance, contact your local fish and game commission for information regarding the status of the fish in your state.

Another method of biological management calls for planting substitute vegetation that is less dense and easier to fish than the grass that has sprung up naturally.

Best example of this came from a pond in northwestern Texas where a shallow neck in a small pond always filled up with thick mats of bushy pondweed. By midsummer, the vegetation would grow more than 50 feet from the shoreline, eliminating almost all fishing and ruining the eye-appeal of the pond.

The pond manager planted lily pads in with the bushy pondweed. In the third year, the pads had outcompeted the bushy pondweed, opening the way to outstanding topwater fishing for bass. What's more, the lily pads are much easier and cheaper to control.

Over time, we may see more use of insects as natural enemies in controlling vegetation. In fact, the Texas Parks and Wildlife is experimenting with a tiny fly from Australia that helps control hydrilla.

The third, and most commonly used, method of aquatic vegetation control is approved chemicals. This is often the fastest means, but it may also be the least desirable. There are times, in fact, when chemicals have worked too quickly, causing water quality problems when the weeds died and decomposed.

At this time, there are no exclusively organic chemicals approved for use for aquatic vegetation control. Over time, introducing chemicals to the water could prove to be an environmental problem.

For this very reason, use only those approved by the EPA for aquatic plants. Follow directions on the label. I've seen some bad, bad fish-kills in waters where the pond managers doubled, even tripled, the prescribed dosage. Consult a biologist before using herbicides.

Most chemicals are selective. In other words, what works on cattails probably won't work on algae. What works on algae may not work on coontail. All the more reason to seek professional direction.

Understanding the difference between habitat and cover, knowing your options, learning your plants and how to control them will help you make solid management decisions for your lake. Better yet, it will help you and your friends and family catch more big fish.

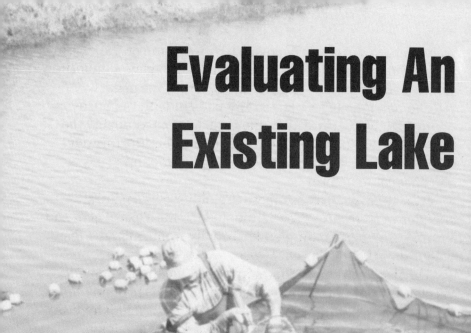

Evaluating An Existing Lake

Sometimes that "dream" lake or pond is not a dream at all. It's a migraine headache you inherited.

Maybe you just bought a weekend retreat that already has a small impoundment on a stream out back. Or you're moving your family back to the old home place that includes a couple ponds.

These puddles are ponds, all right, complete with leaky dams, stunted fish, overgrown weeds and water that stinks. This is the dream pond?

Point is, a high percentage of land owners acquire properties that have existing bodies of water. Some of these waters have been stocked with fish. Almost none has been managed properly.

The new pond owner will take one look, and start searching for help. That's when my phone rings.

One time a man from western Arkansas called our hatchery asking for prices of largemouth bass fingerlings. He was intent on purchasing 300 fingerlings for his four-acre lake.

But after talking with him for a few minutes, hearing that his typical catch was stunted bass, I began to suspect he really didn't need 300 bass fingerlings.

His impression, based on his common sense, was that these particular bass were not growing because they were inferior specimens. Or they were so old they had outlived their usefulness.

He figured he should replace his old stock with

The best lake-management plans begin with a careful analysis of the fish already present in the reservoir. Here, a fisheries crew uses an electroshocking boat to gather fish at dusk.

new, faster-growing fish. To him, this was a problem with his bass.

We continued to talk and I convinced him that we should evaluate his lake before we did anything. Days later, we took a representative sample from the fish population and found that his two-acre pond contained a few large bluegill sunfish and more than 250 skinny black bass measuring 15 to 20 inches in length. We found that his bass were not ancient, but 3 1/2 years old and still in their prime. From charts provided by the Arkansas Game and Fish Commission, I showed him that his bass were more than 30 percent underweight.

A classic case of bass eating themselves out of house and home. His bass were overeating their food chain. In fact, I could tell that the last thing his pond's food chain needed was 300 more mouths to support. The best answer for him was to harvest bass, not stock them!

By surveying his lake with an electroshocking boat and a net, I was able to stop him from making a management mistake—and save him the cost of buying fingerling bass. The new pond owner became a friend and a regular customer, for baitfish and forage, not bass fingerlings.

See? An evaluation gives you a reference point, a place to start. Consider your pond strategy to be a vacation, and the survey is your road map.

Where are you headed? What route are you taking? How much time do you have to get there? What's your budget? With a lake evaluation, you will know. Your trip will be smooth and enjoyable.

If you have an existing lake, evaluate it at least every other year, preferably every year. Even a new lake, stocked with fresh fingerlings, should be sampled after two or three years. It's your 40,000-mile tune-up.

The more you know about your lake and the aquatic environment, the better your management decisions. It may keep you from expensive blunders like I saw at a residential lake near Dallas, Texas, one year.

After you evaluate fish populations, you may decide that the most drastic strategy—draining the lake and starting over—may also be the best.

The phone rang and a woman with the property-owners group laid out the story: The neighborhood was built around a 22-acre lake, but over the past several years, the lake had been covered with an aquatic vegetation. Fishing was hampered. Swimming and boating were out of the question. What once had been a postcard setting had turned to an eyesore.

The lakeside residents appointed a committee, which decided to allow each home owner to control the runaway weeds nearest his own property. On the advice of a county agent, the residents treated the vegetation with chemicals.

The homeowners began spraying the weeds and looking for fast results. The vegetation paused, then continued to spread. One resident was particularly determined, treating the weeds once, twice, three times. The stubborn vegetation held on. Frustrated, he tripled the dose.

Two days later the lake was dotted with the carcasses of ducks, fish, insects, snails and a wide variety of other critters.

Help! Can we control the weeds without devastating the

environment? We agreed to try.

A lake evaluation revealed two types of vegetation, neither affected by the chemicals applied. Wrong diagnosis, wrong treatment.

The triple dosage exceeded the recommended application and shocked the system with toxins. The ducks, mistaking the granules as food, ingested the chemical. Fish, turtles and other organisms dependent on the water for food and shelter had no place to hide.

First thing I did was introduce grass carp to the system, then follow with spot treatments with a legal herbicide. Chemicals have their place in pond management, but only in strictly defined applications, and only after all biological alternatives have been exhausted.

Over the winter, the weeds retreated to allow more normal use of the lake and, yes, migrating mallards have rediscovered their old home. The ducks are back.

These yarns are worth spinning because it shows how important the early evaluation can be. This is particularly true for water analysis.

From a biological and fisheries standpoint you need to know the properties of your water, whether it has the proper pH level to support aquatic life. Is it fertile? Clear or turbid? Does it have a high salt content? Will it produce high-quality fish? A water analysis may give clues.

Most county agents have a listing of labs performing this service. Your agent will have tips on how to package your water for shipping.

Water quality, vegetation, habitat, soil-type—these characteristics fit together to form the fabric of your lake. These factors give your pond its profile, almost like your own personality.

But the one thing most people ask about is their fish.

In order to evaluate the fish, you must gather them in as unbiased fashion, so as not to misrepresent the true picture. Collecting fish by rod and reel, for instance, may be fun, but your use of certain baits tends to concentrate on certain target species. Say you use earthworms on a hook, you are more likely to collect bluegill sunfish while a lake full of bass ignores the offerings. Rod-and-reel sampling can provide insight, but only over an extended period of time. Taken in short spans, this information could lead to false conclusions. To provide the most accurate sample, a random sample is best. Easier said than done. That's why it generally takes a professional fisheries biologist to conduct a reliable evaluation, and that's why he's trained to use several tools.

One is electrofishing equipment. Usually he has a boat with an electrical power source, typically a gasoline powered generator. The boat is rigged with electrodes, or probes, that drop into the water to put the electricity into the lake. The electricity forms a field underwater that temporarily stuns fish that move into it, or fish the field moves over. These fish are picked up, identified, measured, weighed, then gently released into the lake, unharmed.

Electricity, then, is an equal opportunity recruiter. It's blind, unbiased and non-selective, therefore a good method.

It is limited, however, to depths of less than 10 feet, to water with enough suspended particulates to carry electric current. So-called shocking gear may be useless in cattails and other heavy cover where fish may hide.

Since some fish prefer shallow water and others lurk in deeper areas, biologists need other devices.

The shallows are best sampled with a seine, typically 50 feet long, 6 feet wide, with quarter-inch mesh. Here's a chance for the whole family to jump in the pond, get mud between your toes and help the biologist.

By circling shallow areas of water, collecting the fish, then counting and identifying them, you will gather valuable information on which species are reproducing.

In small ponds, make sure to sample three or four areas. This will give you the most accurate reading. In lakes up to 15 acres, you may need to seine four to eight areas. In lakes 30 acres or larger, 15 locations per evaluation should be enough.

For deeper water, ask your professional about gill nets. These tools, generally 150 feet long, come divided into 50-foot sections, six feet wide, starting with half-inch mesh and graduating up to three-inch mesh.

Biologists place the gill net with the "deep end" extending toward the middle of the lake. Fish moving parallel to shore encounter the net and try to go through it. If they can't get their heads through the net, they move to deeper water and continue trying. When they finally find an area where their head will fit, the net, usually made of monofilament line, slides around the gill covers of the fish, effectively trapping the anxious animal. He can't move forward or backward. Again, the fish can be counted, weighed and released unharmed.

A note of caution: Do not leave a gill net in place for long periods of time. The trapped fish will struggle against the mesh and damage themselves or drown. We never leave our nets out longer than two hours, unless it is vital to gather information overnight and we are prepared to lose fish.

Courtesy of Tracker Marine, Springfield, Mo.

No need to wonder about the fertility of this reservoir. Touring pro Rick Clunn shows off a 13-pound, 15-ounce bass taken from a small private lake in central Alabama.

Midsummer is the very best time because all your fish have spawned. It is easier to confirm the presence of certain fish, and it demonstrates your food chain is at peak productivity. Should I mention that seining in June and July warm feels better on the old legs than doing it at Thanksgiving or Easter? Naa.

These services cost $50 to $150 an hour, depending on the equipment used, manpower required and, to some extent, competition with other biologists in the market. It's a bargain. A biologist can quickly gather a tremendous amount of information about your lake, and once you watch a professional evaluate a reservoir, you can do some of it yourself if you're willing to compile the data.

Okay, once some information has been gathered, what

The growth rates of the predator species, such as this largemouth, will tell the lake manager if his strategy is working.

does it mean?

With your goals firmly in mind, see if you have unwanted fish. This is Job One.

Maybe you want to produce largemouth, but you find your pond to be full of common carp. It's a species that may tie up space and nutrients in the water, and hamper your attempts to produce the more popular gamefish. Consult your professional for advice on removing the carp on a selective basis. In extreme cases, he may recommend that you totally renovate the lake, removing all species and starting over from scratch.

In any case, a lake evaluation will provide a basis for these decisions, as well as other tidbits, such as how well your gamefish are growing. Biologists call this age/growth ratio or relative weight. It's simply average weight for a fish at a given length.

Say the average 14-inch bass weighs 1.6 pounds. Use this standard index to compare the weight of your fish to a normal specimen. As long as your fish weigh 90 percent of the standard index, you're okay.

(*Pond Boss* hint: Relative weights may vary by geographic location and growing season. A 10-inch bass in Florida will be slightly heavier than a bass the same length in Michigan.)

From Canada to Louisiana, autumn is best for determining relative weight. In the spring, female fish of most species are heavy-laden with eggs, distorting their true condition and the overall health of the environment.

One day we received a call from a man in Indiana who was managing a flooded mine that was 50 feet deep, with an average depth of 20 feet. Plenty of water. He had owned the property for several years and was trying turn the lake into a trophy bass fishery.

"How do I improve the genetics of my bass?" he asked. "How many adult Florida bass do I stock? And in what size?"

My answers started with a question: In looking at the existing bass population, what size were most of the fish?

The more we visited, the more it became obvious that he had a gang of fish in the 10- to 14-inch range. Too many, in fact.

He knew about his size range by keeping good catch records, which gave me a headstart in helping him. He just didn't understand what the figures meant.

His 14-inch fish were average weight or heavier. Those fish shorter than 10 inches were okay, too. But the middle group, those 10 to 14 inches, were in sad shape. Skinny as eels.

On my recommendation, the fellow stocked Florida bass larger than 15 inches, adult fish in prime spawning condition, at a rate of five per acre just to introduce the Florida gene. He also agreed to eliminate some of the competition for food by removing some of the 10- to 14-inchers he caught on rod and reel.

One nifty method for determining the makeup of your fish population is called the proportion size distribution, or PSD (also called proportional stock density). This helps measure and interpret the dynamics of a population within a species.

Simply put, the PSD measures the quality fish against the

The professional consulting biologist uses several tools and techniques to evaluate a lake, including electroshocking, seining and netting.

population as a whole. Anglers may disagree, but in fisheries jargon a "quality" bass is a largemouth measuring 12 inches or greater. A so-called "trophy" bass is 16 inches or better. Biologists generally say that, in a well-balanced fishery, the PSD range for quality bass should be 40 to 60 percent of the total bass population. If you catch 10 bass in a day, four or five, maybe even six, should be 12 inches long or better. If you manage for trophy bass, the figure should be at least six out of 10, should be even higher than that.

Perhaps you enjoy raising and catching bluegill. The desired balance for these panfish should come out so that 20 to 40 percent of your total catch measures six inches or longer.

If you discover unbalanced figures, consult your biologist or county agent about manipulating the fish population or changing your bag limits. You may want to consider other management techniques, such as removing some of the moss to give your small forage fish less room to hide from hungry bass.

(*Pond Boss* hint: Use only unbiased data, gathered by net, seine, electroshocking or catch records over long periods. If you selectively fish for big fish, and use this for data, your numbers will be tainted.)

One evaluation and management technique we haven't covered is renovation. If, after analysis, you and your professional decide the lake is beyond hope, that its fish population cannot be balanced, you may elect to kill out your reservoir and start again.

Rotenone is one approved fish toxicant that may be used. Anhydrous ammonia is another. These harsh chemicals can have serious, long-term impact on your lake, so it's always best to let the professionals handle them. If you insist on applying these compounds yourself, check with your local authorities and follow the label.

Vegetation may be the final element in lake evaluation we cover here, but it may be foremost in your mind. It can be a serious problem—for boating, for swimming, for fishing, for aesthetics, for property values. In vegetation, however, there are no PSDs, no standard indexes issued by government agencies, no maps issued by the fisheries pros. Instead, it rests with personal preference.

You make the call on how much vegetation you want or need for your lake. Just make sure you do it in conjunction with the evaluation of your fish, your water quality, your soil, the entire pond profile.

How important is evaluation? It's the blueprint for building your lake. Now, Pond Boss, take that first step. Gather as much knowledge as you can about your fishery.

"Only the gamefish swims upstream, but the sensible fish swims down."

— *Ogden Nash*

Attracting Wildlife

Watch closely, especially at dawn or dusk. Your pond may be more than a fish factory, or the site of family reunion cook-outs. It could be a magnet for wildlife.

Developed properly, your lake could attract ducks, geese, songbirds, raccoons and other small mammals, as well as deer, turkey and other wild game animals.

Thrill your friends and family with the sight of a doe tiptoeing to the edge of your pond with its fawn. As they bow to take a drink, you swear you see the antlers of an old buck,

A healthy pond attracts squirrels and other wildlife.

watching from the safety of the woods at water's edge.

Better yet, you can enjoy these sights—and photos— without sacrificing high-quality fishing. In fact, developing a healthy, productive lake improves your chances for luring more free-ranging wildlife. When that happens, a simple family picnic could turn into a short course in nature study.

Wildlife student and habitat stimulator. Angler and lake manager. One practices his or her hobby on dry land, the other on water. But both are conservationists, more alike than they are different.

Consider, then, your options for manipulating the cover and food supply for animals around your lake. Does it provide wild animals something to eat, near the shelter essential to their survival?

Take mourning dove, for example. These migratory visitors are distributed throughout the U.S., qualifying as a gamebird in some states. Anyone who has observed dove knows they love small grain, especially if that food source lies a short flight from ground water—which could be your lake. But a dove will not land around a pond unless he has an open space to land and then walk to the water's edge. These birds seem to like a small beach.

Maybe bobwhite quail stir your interest. This bird seldom needs a drink, drawing moisture from seeds and other food items. Even so, a lake may provide irrigation for some of the plants that put out the quail's favorite menu items.

In many areas of the U.S., puddle ducks such as mallards, wigeon, pintail and teal—the most photogenic species—may be encouraged to visit a pond if shallow-water food is introduced. Sometimes the migratory birds will return to the same watering hole year after year.

Ducks prefer small grains or submerged aquatic vegetation. Attract waterfowl by planting browntop millet at 20 pounds per acre. Japanese millet ranks high on the list of

Many pond owners love to photograph animals in a natural setting.

duck food. Plant this on exposed mud flats without having to turn the soil. Or plant 80 pounds of rice in May through July, and draw the water off the area for 24 to 48 hours. Once the new shoots clear the ground, cover them with six inches of water. Come November, get the camera—or the shotgun.

Wood ducks enjoy some of the same food, but get persnickety about their nesting areas. You may need nesting boxes on pedestals or in trees to hold them for long.

For geese, you'll need shallow, open water far from any brush or other cover that may hold a fox, coyote or bobcat. The goose species—notably Canadas and snows—rank as some of nature's wariest creatures, so you will not likely attract many truly wild birds without the water requirements, coupled with large open grain fields nearby.

Some people introduce domestic geese in an effort to establish a resident population but the birds will end up as honored guests at a coyote banquet if you don't provide them a safe roosting place.

If your lake or pond has an island, build them a simple home by cutting a whiskey barrel in half and placing it upside down. Check with your neighborhood garden supply house. They may sell whiskey barrels for flower pots. Cut a passage hole and add straw. They'll be content and safe, to the point that many private lakes have more mottled, pitiful looking geese than they need.

No island on your lake? Resourceful geese may adopt the pilings of your boat dock.

But maybe you enjoy watching deer. In that case, you may have to forget attracting geese, simply because neither the whitetail nor the mule deer likes to frequent a pond standing in the open, at least not during daylight hours.

Deer are browsers, plucking the tender new growth at ground level and trimming leaves from low tree branches. Acorns, from any one of several oak species, will serve as a natural beacon for deer, as will planting peanuts and other legumes. If you are in deer country and want to feed these critters, try black-eyed peas or clover, planted next to heavy cover.

In many states, particularly in Dixie, it has become quite

Lakeside habitat may be manipulated to attract mourning dove, ducks and other game birds.

popular to attract wildlife through supplementary feeding using commercial ration. In the Rocky Mountain West, some pond owners lure into camera range everything from elk to pronghorn antelope, plus dozens of other smaller non-game species. Some states ban the use of feeders in hunting, but none prohibit them for nature study or photography.

Ducks, geese, dove, quail, wild hogs, deer...With habitat manipulation, these species may be drawn to your lake. See your county agent or consulting biologist for the best plants for wildlife in your area.

Glossary

ACRE-FOOT — a measurement used in calculating volume of water. The amount of water that covers one surface acre one foot deep. One acre foot of water is 325,829 gallons.

ADULT FISH — sexually mature fish, not necessarily related to size.

ALKALINITY — alkaline condition, the quality that constitutes an alkali; alkali is the measurement of any of a number of the various bases, usually the hydroxides of the alkali metals. In pond water, this usually refers to the amount of calcium hydroxide.

ANGLER — anyone who fishes with a pole or rod-and-reel.

AQUACULTURIST — a person engaged in the production of aquatic animals, usually for profit.

AQUATIC COMMUNITY — all living things, plant, insect, animal, that derive at least part of the requirements for life in a given pond. This refers to the entire food chain, from plankton to vegetation to insects to fish and other aquatic animals.

AQUATIC VEGETATION — any of the plants living in or around water, from three basic types—submersed (under the surface), emersed (growing above the water line) and floating.

BACKCROSS — an animal produced by the genetic blend with another animal of different genetic makeup, often its own parents. Generally, this refers to a genetically inferior animal.

BALANCED FISHERY — a state of equilibrium among fish species, with sufficient prey to support predators of varying sizes. Neither group outcompetes the other for space or food.

BIOLOGICALLY PRODUCTIVE — a pond in which living organisms flourish.

BOTTOM-WATER RELEASE — management technique using a drain pipe system to drain excess water the from lake from the bottom. This removes the least desirable water in a lake, while preserving fresh incoming water.

CARNIVORE — meat eater. In a pond, this could be anything from a largemouth bass to a great blue heron to a turtle.

CONSERVATIONIST — one who works to manage natural resources.

COVER — man-made objects such as cinder blocks placed under water primarily to congregate fish for the benefit of fishermen. Anglers call this "structure."

CRUSTACEANS — animals in an aquatic system that have a shell. Snails, crawfish, freshwater shrimp and mussels all fit into this category

DENITRIFY — the natural process of breaking down the nitrogen waste products of metabolism.

DRAWDOWN — lowering the water level in a lake, generally to accomplish a specific management goal such as identifying fish in a pond and removing the least desirable species.

ELECTROPHORESIS — the motion of tissue suspended in a fluid medium due to the influence of an electrical field. Biologists use this laboratory technique to identify genetic strains of fish, especially the Florida strain largemouth bass.

ENVIRONMENT — all physical things, conditions or influences surrounding a lake or pond.

FERTILITY — the measurement of nutrients in a body of water. In private waters, this generally refers to the production of plankton or "bloom" in the water.

FILTER FEEDER — animals such as the bighead carp that derive nutrition by gleaning their food from the water.

FOOD CHAIN — a series of organisms interrelated in their feeding habits. In a pond, the small species generally provide a food supply for the next larger species, which in turn, provide food for the larger animals.

FORAGE FISH — species such as the fathead minnow that serve as food for predators.

FREEBOARD — the distance from the surface of the water or spillway to the top of the dam.

HABITAT — the native environment of an animal or plant, the place where it lives.

HARDNESS — the measurement of quality of impure water imparted by the presence of dissolved salts, especially calcium sulfate or bicarbonate. Ponds in West Texas, for instance, have hard water.

HERBIVORE — an animal that only eats plants.

HYBRID — the offspring of parents from different species.

INTERGRADE — an offspring of two parents, same species but different strains. In ponds, the Florida bass will cross with native northern bass.

LAKE MANAGER — a conservationist who uses nature to enhance a lake toward a specific set of goals.

OPPORTUNISTIC OMNIVORE — any animal that prefers meat, but will eat what it can find in order to survive. Teenage boys and girls fit this description. So does the channel catfish.

pH — measurement of content of free hydrogen ions, the acid content of water. On a scale of 1 to 14, with 7 as neutral, a pH reading of less than 7 means the water is acidic.

PLANKTON — microscopic plants and animals suspended, floating or drifting in a body of water. In lake management plankton this provides the base to the food chain.

PREDATOR — an animal that eats other animals.

PSD — Proportion Stock Density or Percentage Size Distribution. Fisheries biologists use this measurement to evaluate a fish population by size.

ROTENONE — an organic product, derived from the root of the

Derris plant used as a fish toxicant. This product is used to remove fish, generally from an old lake badly in need of renovation.

SAC FRY — a newly hatched fish that relies on the remnants of the yolk in its own egg for nutrition.

SPORTFISH — any fish sought by anglers for recreation.

STRATIFICATION — the layering of water, usually according to temperature. In freshwater lakes, cold water sinks, creating bands in a layer cake effect.

SWIM-UP FRY — the stage in the development of a newly hatched fish when it has absorbed the yolk in its own egg and has begun swimming freely. Generally, the fish, after absorbing the sac, swims away from the nest to seek food.

THERMOCLINE — the thin defining line between layers of a stratified body of water.

TRIPLOID GRASS CARP — a white amur that has been genetically altered by adding an extra set of chromosomes to render it sterile. In pond management, this fish helps control aquatic vegetation.

TURBIDITY — a measurement of the particulates suspended in water. A murky pond generally has a rich plankton content or its bottom sediments have been stirred by wind and wave action.

WATERSHED — the amount of land that drains rainfall runoff into a lake.

Wr — the symbol for relative weight, a measurement used by fisheries biologists to compare individuals in a fish population to a standard for that type and length of fish in an average situation.

Notes:

Notes:

Notes:

Notes: